D1030280

Katie's Chickens

Alfred A. Knopf  New York

Katie's CHICKENS

Nancy Dingman Watson

ILLUSTRATIONS BY

Aldren A. Watson

TO JEAN STRACHAN WILSON

L. C. Catalog card number: 65-22003

This is a Borzoi Book, published by Alfred A. Knopf, Inc.

 Manufactured in the United States of America, and distributed by Random House, Inc.
Published simultaneously in Toronto, Canada, by Random House of Canada, Limited.

Katie's Chickens

Here comes Katie.
She has a dish of table scraps.
The scraps are for her chickens.

Katie's chickens live in the barnyard.
Katie has a fat brown mother hen. She has a big father rooster with a red comb and a long tail.
The father rooster sits on the fence.
He crows, "*Cock-a-doodle-doo!*"

The hen and the rooster scratch and peck the ground.
They are looking for grains of corn.
They run through the tall grass after bugs.
They dig in the garden for worms.

Katie chases butterflies and digs for worms, too.
But she can’t catch the butterflies
and she puts the worms back for when she goes fishing.

The brown hen has a nest hidden in the hay of the barn.
Every day she lays a beautiful pink-brown egg in her nest.
Then she clucks proudly to say, "I have seven beautiful eggs
in my nest today. But my nest is hidden away.
Nobody knows where my nest is."

But Katie knows!

One day the mother hen does not come out to scratch and peck the ground.
She is sitting on her nest keeping her eggs warm.
Inside each egg a baby chick is growing.
Mother Hen cannot see her babies growing inside the eggs.
But she knows she must keep them warm and protected.

Outdoors, Father Rooster crows loudly to the hen,
"Come out into the barnyard and scratch for me!"
But the mother hen will not come out.
Katie says, "Come out in the sunshine
and run through the tall grass with me!"
But the mother hen will not budge.

All day she sits quietly on her nest in a dark corner.
In the evening the rooster calls again.
“Nighttime is coming. Come sit on the roost beside me and keep me warm!”
But the mother hen will not move.

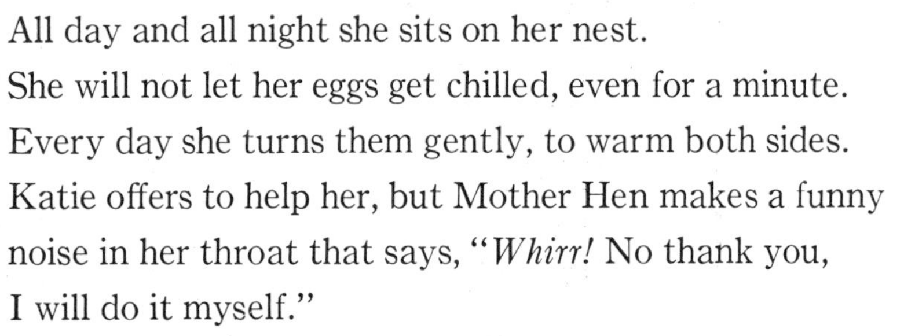

All day and all night she sits on her nest.
She will not let her eggs get chilled, even for a minute.
Every day she turns them gently, to warm both sides.
Katie offers to help her, but Mother Hen makes a funny
noise in her throat that says, "*Whirr!* No thank you,
I will do it myself."

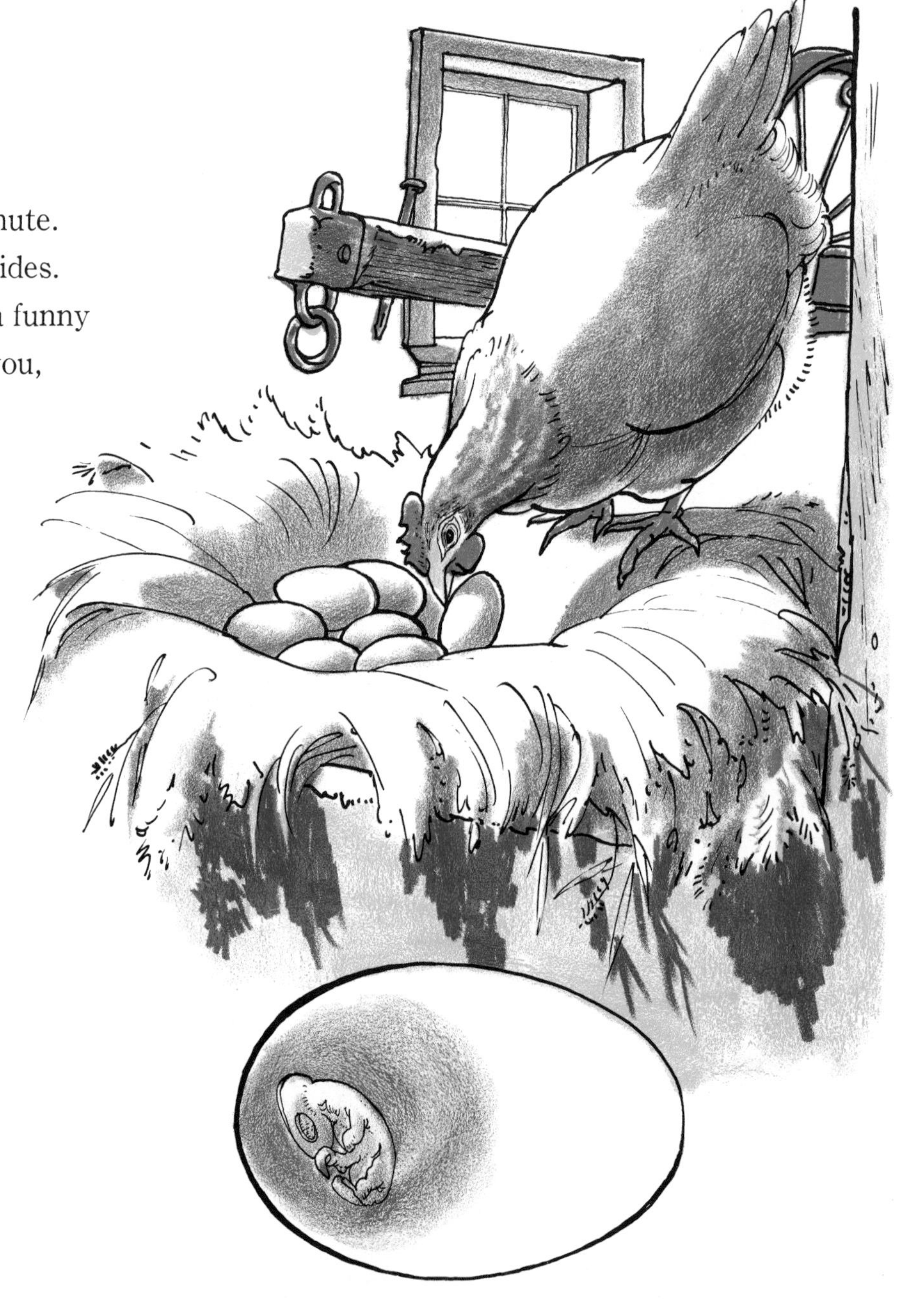

Katie's big dog barks at Mother Hen. "I'll give you
a head start if you'll let me chase you!"
But Mother Hen does not even blink her eye.

Katie's kitten tumbles from a rafter and lands on Mother Hen's back. "*Squawk!*" says the mother hen, and pecks the kitten on the nose. "*Me-oww!*" cries the kitten. The hen scolds a minute, then she settles down again gently.

Katie would like to peek under and see the eggs.
If Katie moves very quietly, Mother Hen lets her feel
the warm, soft feathers of her breast, and the
smooth-shelled eggs beneath. The feathers keep the eggs safe
from breaking. They keep them warm at night
when the sun goes down and the barn is cold.

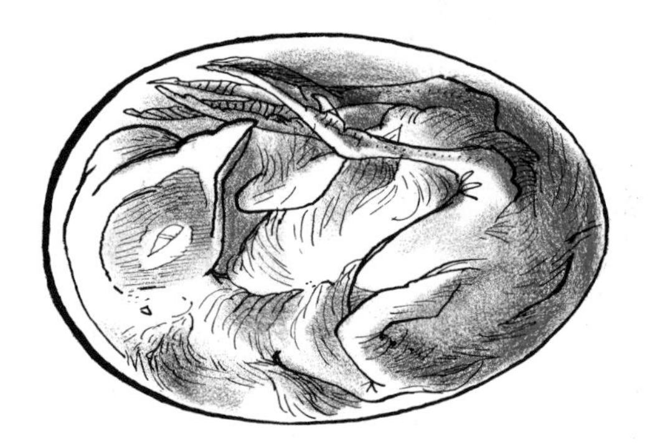

Katie thinks the hen must be lonely, so she stays a long time. Each day she brings food and water to the hen, who will not leave her nest even to eat.

Father Rooster crows every morning, "Come outdoors!
The sun is warm. It feels good on my back.
The bugs are fat and juicy today.
The corn is golden and good."
But nothing will tempt Mother Hen to leave her eggs.

Every day Katie peeks under the patient hen.
Katie does not think there will *ever* be any baby chickens.
But at last, after twenty-one days, the little chickens
have grown to fill the inside of the eggshells.
They have used up all the food inside the eggs.
Now they must leave the eggs and go outside,
for room to grow and food to eat.

Katie can hear them pecking and pecking inside the rosy
brown shells. *Tap-tap-tap!*
"How will they ever get out?" says Katie to the mother hen.
But the little chicks inside the eggs have
strong neck muscles. They have sharp little beaks with
a special hard bump for breaking the shell.

They peck and peck at the inside of their shells.
Tap-tap-tap! Soon a crack appears in one shell,
then in another. The baby chicks rest when they get tired.
Then they peck harder than ever. Little holes break open,
and Katie can see the tiny wet chicks inside the shells.
They seem to be all feet and legs!

At last one shell pops apart. A little chicken half falls,
half climbs out.
It is a weak little chicken, all wet and scraggly.
Katie tries to dry it off with a doll towel.

Soon another and another egg breaks open.
Now Katie has seven little baby chicks to take care of!
When the little chicks are dry and warm and rested,
Mother Hen gets off the nest.
She stretches her long legs and flaps her wings.
It has been a long time!

Now Katie's little chickens are fluffy and yellow.
They run about the barn floor and jump on their mother's back.
Mother Hen clucks to her babies.
She leads them cautiously out of the barn
and into the sunshine.

She squawks a warning to the big dog, the saucy kitten, and even to Father Rooster. "Just don't come too close!" she says severely.

Katie marches in front of the hen and chicks.
She is proud too.
The little chickens are happy to stretch and run in new places.
They flap their tiny wings
and scratch the earth with their small feet.
They pick up bits of seeds just as Mother Hen does.

Katie sprinkles chicken feed on the ground. The mother hen calls her babies with a high "*Chirrup!*"
How excited they get! Two of them pretend to fight, standing beak to beak and stretching their pink toes to make themselves tall.
Their mother shows them how to drink from a puddle, and tip up their feathered heads to let the water run down their throats.

Mother Hen clucks comfortably to them.
"Stay near me," she says. "Don't wander away.
You are very little. You might get lost."
But Mother Hen does not mind when Katie holds a baby chick
very carefully.

All day Katie and the little chickens run and play, eat and eat.
Katie shares her picnic lunch with them.
When she lies down in the grass they run over her
and tickle her arms and face and legs.

But now the sun is going down.
Katie's mother calls her for supper.
Soon it will be bedtime.
The mother hen calls to her baby chickens.
It is bedtime for them, too.
They follow Katie and their mother back toward the barn.
Katie wants to help tuck them in, before she goes to bed.
The mother hen walks with stately step up the bank
to the barn, scolding all the way.
The little chickens waltz and skip around her.

Now they are back in their warm nest.
Mother Hen nestles down in the hay.
She lifts up her wings and clucks to her babies.
The little chickens creep under the soft feathers and down of her breast. They jostle and squabble for the best spot.

One little fellow peeps out of the feathers on his mother's back. How did he get up there?

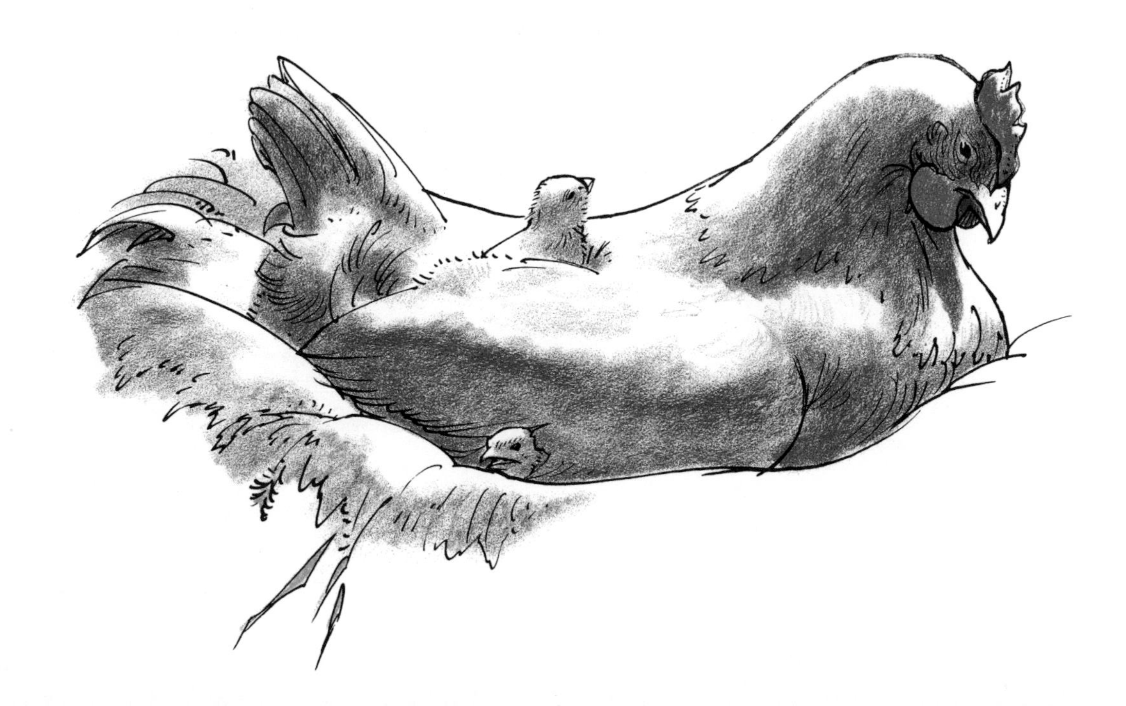

But it is nighttime, and soon they settle down to sleep.
The mother hen makes gentle clucking noises,
like a chicken lullaby.
Katie tucks extra hay around the nest.
Then she tiptoes out of the barn and up to the house.
Her mommy wants to give her supper and tuck her into bed, too.

Tomorrow the little chicks will be up at dawn with Katie,
eating and playing and growing.
Some day they will grow into big hens and roosters.
Then they will be mothers and fathers, too.
But now they are just little chicks, one day old,
sleeping happily under their mother's wing.

Text set in Century Old Style 157. *Composed at* Eastern Typesetting Company, Hartford, Conn.
Printed by Connecticut Printers, Hartford, Conn. *Bound by* A. Horowitz, Clifton, New Jersey